The Enormous Turnip

Phonic Readers AGE 4-6 LEVEL 2

Autumn Publishing

Once upon a time, an old man planted some turnip s**ee**ds.

Then, a w**ee**k went by. Some tiny turnips were p**ee**ping throug[h]
The old man could s**ee** thr**ee** turnips, but one was different.

Focus on the
ee sound
(as in s**ee**ds)
as you read.

Wh**ee**!

2

The other little turnips grew r**oo**ts and sh**oo**ts, but the enormous turnip s**oo**n looked fully grown.

I think it'll reach the m**oo**n s**oo**n.

After a st**or**m, the turnip grew even m**or**e en**or**mous. It started to squash the sweetc**or**n.

Focus on the **or** sound (as in h**or**se) as you read.

One m**or**ning, the old man went to look f**or** his garden f**or**k to dig up the turnip.

It's now **or** never!

or

Can you spot these 5 items somewhere in the scene?

Place the stickers from your sticker sheet here as you find each one.

st**or**m

h**or**se

f**or**k

d**oo**r

sweetc**or**n

Nice

work

or

7

The old man heaved as he struggled with the enormous, p**ur**ple t**ur**nip.

Suddenly, he felt a b**ur**ning pain in his back. He t**ur**ned to his wife and groaned.

I need a n**ur**se!

Focus on the **ur** sound (as in t**ur**nip) as you read.

No, we need that t**ur**nip!

Can you spot these 5 items somewhere in the scene?

Place the stickers from your sticker sheet here as you find each one.

t**ur**nip

c**ur**tains

t**ur**key

p**ur**se

f**ur**ry

Good job

"Okay, my d**ear**," said the old man.
"We can get this turnip, never f**ear**."

When you h**ear** me say PULL, then pull hard!

Focus on the **ear** sound (as in b**ear**d) as you read.

So, the man's wife stood n**ear** his r**ear** and pulled.

ear

Can you spot these 5 items somewhere in the scene?

Place the stickers from your sticker sheet here as you find each one.

ear

y**ear**

r**ear**

t**ear**

b**ear**d

Well done

ear

11

Then, the old woman saw a boy wit[h] a bag of **gr**a**in**. "Our **aim** is to pull [up] this turnip," she expl**ai**ned.

Wait until I give the signal!

Focus on the **ai** sound (as in gr**ai**n) as you read.

o, the boy with the gr**ai**n pulled
he old woman's w**ai**st, but the
urnip did not move.

ai

Can you spot
these 5 items
somewhere in
the scene?

Place the stickers
from your sticker
sheet here as you
find each one.

t**ai**l

sn**ai**l

r**ai**nbow

gr**ai**n

n**ai**l

Nice

work

ai

13

Next, a girl came d**ow**n from the t**ow**n. "H**ow** can I help?" she asked.

"You can pull right n**ow**, that's h**ow**!" cried everyone.

The girl gave a b**ow** and h**ow** she pulled.

N**ow**, everyon
PULL!

Focus on the **ow** sound (as in c**ow**) as you read.

14

ow

Can you spot these 5 items somewhere in the scene?

Place the stickers from your sticker sheet here as you find each one.

cow

town

crown

flower

owl

Good job

ow

15

The girl saw a g**oa**t across the r**oa**d. She took some **oa**ts to feed the g**oa**t and led it to the garden.

Focus on the **oa** sound (as in **oa**ts) as you read.

16

Pages 2-3

Pages 4-5

Pages 6-7

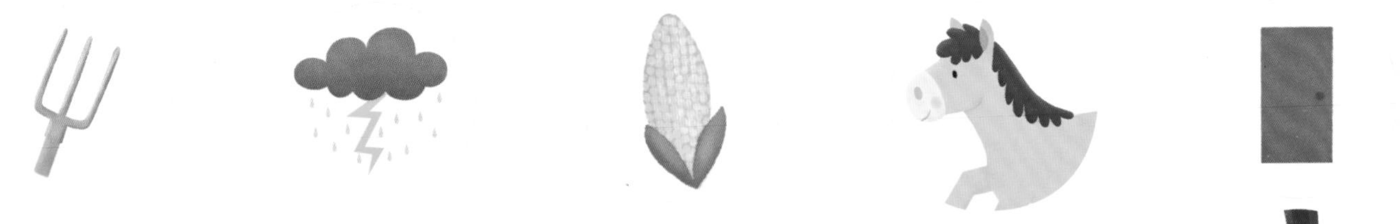

Pages 8-9

Pages 10-11

Jan | Feb | Mar | Apr
May | Jun | Jul | Aug
Sep | Oct | Nov | Dec

Pages 12-13

Pages 14-15

Pages 16-17

Pages 18-19

Pages 20-21
Pages 22-23
Pages 24-25

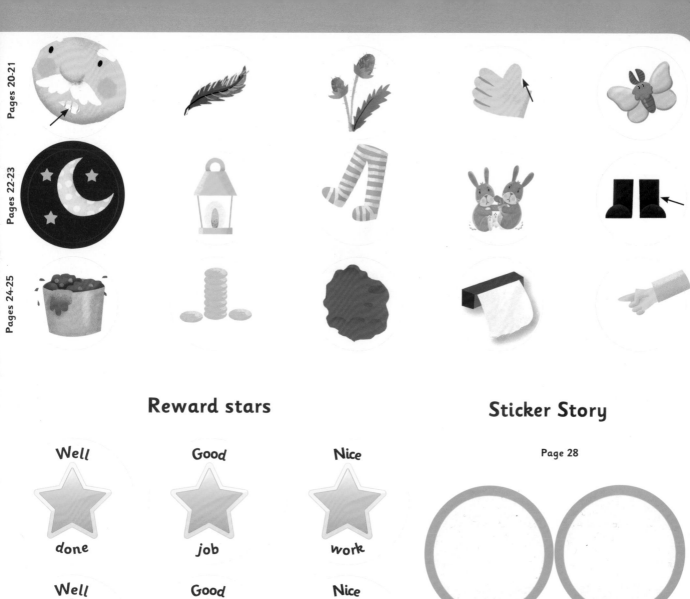

Reward stars

Well

done

Good

job

Nice

work

Well

done

Good

job

Nice

work

Well

done

Good

job

Nice

work

Nice

work

Sticker Story

Page 28

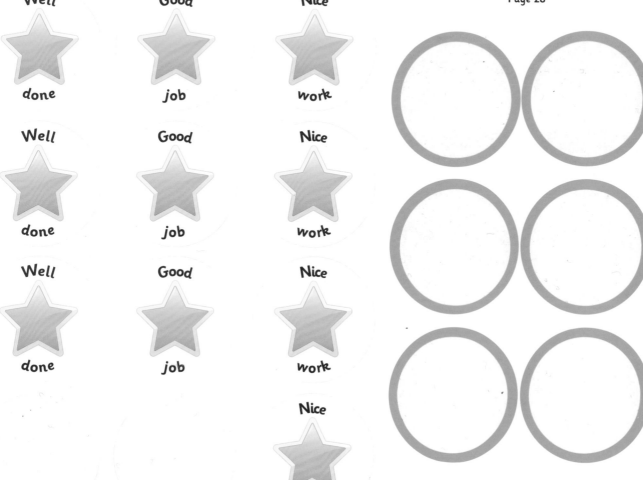

Goat, hold onto my coat.

So the goat held on and pulled, but the turnip did not move.

Can you spot these 5 items somewhere in the scene?

Place the stickers from your sticker sheet here as you find each one.

toad

coat

goat

road

oats

Well done

oa

17

Suddenly, there was a barking sound in the yard. It was Farmer Martin's farm dog. The farm dog was called Barker. He came over and held on to the goat.

Barker, pull as hard as you can.

Focus on the **ar** sound (as in b**ar**n) as you read.

18

ar

Can you spot these 5 items somewhere in the scene?

Place the stickers from your sticker sheet here as you find each one.

jar

barn

arm

star

yard

Nice work

ar

19

So, **the** old man, **the** old woman, **the** girl, **the** goat and **the** dog all pulled.

Pull **the** dog's tail!

Focus on the **th** sound (as in mo**th**) as you read.

They **th**ought **th**e turnip would come out, but it didn't.

Then, Be**th** **th**e cat came out to help.

th
Can you spot these 5 items somewhere in the scene?

Place the stickers from your sticker sheet here as you find each one.

mo**th**

thistles

thumb

tee**th**

fea**th**er

Good

⭐

job

th

21

The enormous turnip was still stuck t**igh**t that n**igh**t.

Then, under the br**igh**t moonl**igh**t, a tiny mouse appeare
It held the cat's tail in its little teeth and pulled.

Focus on the
igh sound
(as in n**igh**t)
as you read.

At last, the enormous turnip came right out of the ground.

igh

Can you spot these 5 items somewhere in the scene?

Place the stickers from your sticker sheet here as you find each one.

ti**gh**ts

ni**gh**t

ri**gh**t

fi**gh**t

li**gh**t

Well done

igh

23

So, they cleaned off the **s**oil and **b**oiled some turnip to make soup.

They covered the rest in **f**oil so it wouldn't sp**oil**. Then, the neighbours came for a turnip party!

Focus on the **oi** sound (as in s**oil**) as you read.

24

oi

Can you spot these 5 items somewhere in the scene?

Place the stickers from your sticker sheet here as you find each one.

coins

point

soil

boil

foil

Nice work

oi

25

I Spy Sounds

Play a game of I Spy, using the sounds on the right and the pictures below.

ow/ar/oi/oa/igh

Are there any pictures that don't contain any of these sounds?

When you spot a picture that contains one of the sounds, say the word out loud.

Sticker Story

Read the story, using the stickers from your sticker sheet to fill in the gaps.

Once, an old man planted some  s**ee**ds.

One grew bigger **th**an **the** o**th**ers.

After a  , it grew to be en**or**mous.

The man and his wife n**ee**ded help

to pull up **the** t**ur**nip. **Th**ey saw a boy wi**th** a

bag of  , a girl from  and a

A cat and a mouse helped **th**em all pull, until

the t**ur**nip came out of **the** ground, covered in  .

Phonic Lines

Follow the lines to join the pictures to the correct words, then say the sound each one contains.

turkey

snail

cow

Rhyming Pictures

Match up each picture on the left to the one that rhymes with it on the right.

goat

nail

town

tree

tail

bee

coat

crown

Tell a Story

Look at the pictures and tell the story from memory.
What sounds can you remember?

Phonic Moments

Fill in the key sound words for each picture below. What happened in these parts of the story?